I Have, Who Has?

LANGUAGE ARTS

D1129998

Written by
Trisha Callella

Editor: Dorothy Ly
Cover Illustrator: Nancy Carlson
Design/Production: Alicia Triche
Art Director: Moonhee Pak
Project Director: Stacey Faulkner

Table of Contents

I HAVE, WHO HAS? is a series of books that provide reinforcement with various academic skills through group activities. These activities consist of game cards that students read and interactively answer. The 12 games included in this resource will help students improve listening skills, build vocabulary, and strengthen standards-based language arts skills and strategies. Also included are reproducible activities to reinforce skills practiced in select games. Use the reproducible pages for review practice, assessments, or homework.

Each game consists of either 12 or 18 cards based on the skill. Play the game as a whole class, small group, or by having children partner up depending on the skill level or size of the class. The skills and concepts addressed in this resource include:

- Letter recognition
- Beginning letter–sound correspondence
- Ending letter–sound correspondence
- Rhyming words
- Word families
- High frequency words
- Vocabulary development
- Sentence structure

The ready-to-use card stock game cards require minimal preparation and allow you to begin using *I Have, Who Has?* today. Each game is color-coded for easy sorting and cleanup. These engaging games are sure to keep children involved as they learn valuable language skills.

Getting Started

PREPARING AND ORGANIZING GAME MATERIALS

1) Photocopy a set of the game cards before you pull them apart. This is your reference to the correct game card order. The cards are printed in order from left to right and top to bottom. You may also want to make overhead transparencies as a visual reference to help children follow the game.

2) Separate the cards along the perforated lines and laminate them for durability.

3) Place each game in an envelope or sandwich-size resealable plastic bag labeled with the game name. Store games in a plastic or cardboard shoebox, or in zippered pencil pouches in a 3-ring notebook.

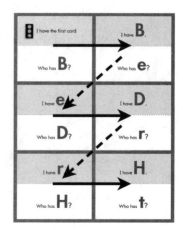

INSTRUCTIONS FOR GAME PLAY

1) When introducing a game for the first time, it is recommended that you review the language skill(s) and vocabulary prior to game play.

2) With the children, practice saying the *I have... Who has...* sentence phrasing for the game being introduced. The sentence frames provide the necessary language for successful game play and are provided in small print for those children who can read. Refer to pages 5 and 6 for the sentence frames for each game.

3) Mix up the cards. Pass out at least one card to each child. If you have more children than cards, have some children share their cards with a classmate.

4) Have the child with the first game card (identified by a traffic signal with a green light) begin the game by saying *I have the first card. Who has...?* As each child reads a card, monitor your copy to make sure children are reading the cards in the correct order. Use colored overhead transparencies and cover all cards except the one being read. Or use a document camera to display each card immediately after each child has read his or her card. This will help the children follow along when playing a game for the first time. If children correctly match each card, then the last card will "loop" back to the first card.

ADDITIONAL WAYS TO USE THE CARDS

POCKET CHART OR MAGNETIC BOARD CENTERS
Use the cards as a manipulative center with a pocket chart. Have the children arrange the cards in the correct order in the pocket chart. Or create a magnetic board center by photocopying the cards on card stock and attaching a magnet to each one. Have the children place the cards in the correct order on a magnetic whiteboard.

PARENT VOLUNTEERS AND SUBSTITUTE TEACHERS
Once the games have been introduced, have parent volunteers play them with small groups of students who need extra practice with specific skills. Or store the games in a designated area for substitute teachers to use as filler activities. The reproducible pages can be used as follow-up enrichment.

SCHOOL–TO–HOME CONNECTION
Send a game home in a storage pouch along with a description about how the game was played in class and how it can be played at home by lining the cards up correctly. You might want to have a simple form for parents to give brief feedback about how the game play went.

NAME THAT LETTER!

18 cards

Sentence Frame: I have lowercase/uppercase *(student reads the letter)*. Who has lowercase/uppercase *(student reads the letter)?*

Standards reinforced: letter recognition, distinguishing uppercase and lowercase letters

Extension: Play the game again. Challenge the class to name the letter that comes before and after the letter read on the card before continuing to the next card in the game.

Reproducible: Page 7

Note: Capital and lowercase letters that are formed the same, but only vary in size, have been omitted from the game.

BEGINNING SOUNDS

ODD ONE OUT

18 cards

Sentence Frame: I have *(student names the picture)*. Who has the odd one out? *(student names the 3 picture choices)*

Standards reinforced: sound matching, sound discrimination

Extension: Play the game again. After each "I have…" card is read, challenge the class to name a third word with the same beginning sound before continuing to the next question in the game.

Reproducible: Page 8

BEGINNING SOUND MATCH

18 cards

Sentence Frame: I have *(student names the picture)*. Who has the same first sound as *(student names the picture)?*

Standards reinforced: matching beginning letter sounds, sound discrimination

Extension: Play the game again. After each "I have…" statement is read, challenge the class to name two other words that start with the same sound before continuing to the next clue in the game.

WHAT LETTER DO I BEGIN WITH?

18 cards

Sentence Frame: I have *(student reads the letter)*. Who has the first letter in *(student names the picture)?*

Standards reinforced: sound discrimination, letter-sound correspondence

Extension: Play the game again. Give each child a dry-erase board and marker. After each child reads the question, have the other children guess the answer by writing down the first letter in the word on their boards. Once the answer is revealed by the next child, have the children give silent cheers if their guesses match the correct letter.

Reproducible: Page 9

ANIMAL NAMES

18 cards

Sentence Frame: I have *(student names the picture)*. Who has the zoo/farm/ocean animal that begins with *(student reads the letter)?*

Standards reinforced: letter–sound correspondence, categorization of animals, vocabulary development

Extension: When the game is finished, ask students to share an animal from one of the three types of animal groups in the game (zoo, farm, ocean) and say the beginning letter sound of the animal name.

Reproducible: Page 10

RHYME TIME

18 cards

Sentence Frame: I have *(student names the picture)*. Who has the picture that rhymes with *(student names the picture)?*

Standards reinforced: rhyming, sound discrimination, vocabulary development

Extension: Play the game again. After each "I have..." sentence is read, challenge the class to name two other rhyming words before continuing to the next clue in the game.

WORD FAMILIES

ODD ONE OUT

12 cards

Sentence Frame: I have *(student names the picture)*. Who has the odd one out? *(student names the 3 picture choices)*

Standards reinforced: sound discrimination, sound matching, rhyming, recognizing like and unlike word parts, vocabulary development

Extension: Play the game again. After the "I have…" sentence is read, challenge the class to name two other words that start with the same sound before continuing to the next clue in the game.

Reproducible: Page 11

COLORS

12 cards

Sentence Frame: I have *(student reads the color word)*. Who has *(student says the color)*?

Standards reinforced: reading color words, matching colors to color words

Extension: Play the game again, but have the child reading the "Who has . . ." part spell the color word instead of read it.

Reproducible: Page 12

WHERE AM I?

12 cards

Sentence Frame: I have the cat *(student describes where the cat is)*. Who has the cat *(student describes where the cat is)*?

Standards reinforced: reading and understanding positional words, vocabulary development

Extension: After students play the game, give each child a red, blue, and yellow bear counter. Then provide a clue such as *The red bear is behind the blue bear.* Have students arrange their corresponding colored bears into the correct positions.

Reproducible: Page 13

ODD WORD OUT

18 cards

Sentence Frame: I have *(student reads the word)*. Who has the odd one out? *(student reads the 4 word choices)*

Standards reinforced: reading high frequency words, automaticity in recognizing high frequency words

Extension: Play the game again. Give each child a dry-erase board. After the "Who has...?" question is read, have the children write down the first letter in the answer. After the "I have..." answer is read, have children give silent cheers if the letters they wrote match.

Reproducible: Page 14

I CAN READ!

18 cards

Sentence Frame: I have *(student names the picture)*. Who has *(student says the letters in the word)*?

Standards reinforced: identifying CVC words, alphabetic principle, phoneme substitution, vocabulary development

Extension: Use magnetic letters on a white board to model making CVC words by only changing one letter at a time as the game proceeds.

Reproducible: Page 15

I CAN SPELL!

12 cards

Sentence Frame: I have *(student says the letters in the word)*. Who has the letters in the word *(student reads the word)*?

Standards reinforced: spelling high frequency words, concepts of print (letters vs. words), reading high frequency words, automaticity in recognizing high frequency words

Extension: Play the game again. Give each child a dry-erase board. After the child reads the "Who has … " question, have the other children write the word on their boards.

Reproducible: Page 16

Letter Match

Draw a line to match the uppercase letter to the lowercase letter.

A •	• c	B •	• d
C •	• h	D •	• g
F •	• a	E •	• j
H •	• k	G •	• e
K •	• f	J •	• b
I •	• s	L •	• m
N •	• n	R •	• l
P •	• v	O •	• t
S •	• p	M •	• o
V •	• i	T •	• r
Q •	• y	W •	• u
X •	• q	U •	• z
Y •	• x	Z •	• w

Beginning Sounds

Say the name of each picture. Cross out the picture that does **not** begin with the same sound.

①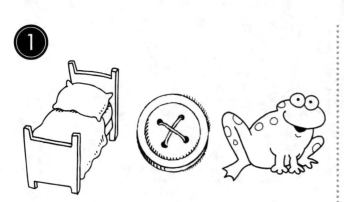

②

③

④

⑤

⑥

⑦

⑧

I Know Who I Am • Language Arts & Gr. K © 2010 Creative Teaching Press

What Letter Do I Begin With?

Say the name of each picture. Write the letter it begins with on the line.

   _____

 _____

  _____

 _____

  _____

 _____

  _____

  _____

Name _____ Date _____

Animal Names

Say the name of each animal. Write the letter(s) it begins with on the line.

①  _____

②  _____

③  _____

④  _____

⑤  _____

⑥ 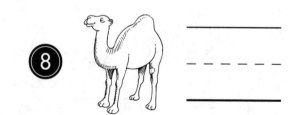 _____

⑦  _____

⑧  _____

Word Families

Say the name of each picture. Cross out the picture that does **not** have the same ending sound.

 1

 2

 3

4

 5

 6

 7

 8

Name _____   Date _____

Colors

Read the word. Trace the word. Color the picture to match the word.

red

brown

black

yellow

orange

green

Where Am I?

Choose a word from the box that describes where the cat is.
Write the word on the line.

on	under	between	behind	in	by

Odd Word Out

Read the words in each box. Circle the same words.
Write the odd word out on the line.

 1 | can   my   can   can

_____
- - - - - - - - - - - - - -
_____

 2 | to   the   the   the

_____
- - - - - - - - - - - - - -
_____

 3 | like   is   like   like

_____
- - - - - - - - - - - - - -
_____

 4 | at   at   at   see

_____
- - - - - - - - - - - - - -
_____

 5 | me   you   you   you

_____
- - - - - - - - - - - - - -
_____

 6 | and   and   for   and

_____
- - - - - - - - - - - - - -
_____

Name _____ Date _____

I Can Read!

Read the word. Circle the picture that matches.

① rat

② man

 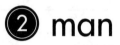

③ hat

④ can

⑤ bat

⑥ fan

⑦ mat

⑧ pan

 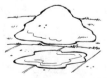 

Name _____ Date _____

I Can Spell!

Read the word. Spell the word out loud as you trace it. Write the word.

1 at

2 see

3 like

4 my

5 am

6 can

I have the first card.

Who has **B**?

I have **B**.

Who has **e**?

I have **e**.

Who has **D**?

I have **D**.

Who has **r**?

I have **r**.

Who has **H**?

I have **H**.

Who has **t**?

I have **t**.

Who has **Y**?

I have **Y**.

Who has **f**?

I have **f**.

Who has **M**?

I have **M**.

Who has **i**?

I have **i**.

Who has **G**?

I have **G**.

Who has **I**?

I have **I**.

Who has **Q**?

I have **Q**.

Who has **j**?

I have **j**.

Who has **A**?

I have **A**.

Who has **n**?

I have **n**.

Who has **K**?

I have **K**.

 Who has the first card?

I have the first card.

Who has the odd one out?

I have  .

Who has the odd one out?

I have  .

Who has the odd one out?

I have  .

Who has the odd one out?

I have  .

Who has the odd one out?

I have  .

Who has the odd one out?

I have  .

Who has the odd one out?

I have  .

Who has the odd one out?

I have  .

Who has the odd one out?

I have  .

Who has the odd one out?

I have  .

Who has the odd one out?

I have  .

Who has the odd one out?

I have  .

Who has the odd one out?

I have  .

Who has the odd one out?

I have  .

Who has the odd one out?

I have  .

Who has the odd one out?

I have  .

Who has the odd one out?

I have  .

 Who has the first card?

I have the first card.

Who has the same first sound as ball?

I have

Who has the same first sound as soap?

I have

Who has the same first sound as dog?

I have

Who has the same first sound as shoe?

I have

Who has the same first sound as penguin?

I have

Who has the same first sound as turtle?

I have

Who has
the same
first sound
as heart?

I have

Who has
the same
first sound
as cow?

I have

Who has
the same
first sound
as fork?

I have

Who has
the same
first sound
as rose?

I have

Who has
the same
first sound
as apple?

I have

Who has
the same
first sound
as goat?

I have

Who has the same first sound as map?

I have

Who has the same first sound as zipper?

I have

Who has the same first sound as nest?

I have

Who has the same first sound as leaf?

I have

Who has the same first sound as jam?

I have

Who has the first card?

I have the first card.

Who has the first letter in monkey?

I have **m**.

Who has the first letter in sock?

I have **s**.

Who has the first letter in ring?

I have **r**.

Who has the first letter in foot?

I have **f**.

Who has the first letter in horse?

I have **h**.

Who has the first letter in peach?

I have **p**.

Who has the
first letter in
zoo?

I have **z**.

Who has the
first letter in
book?

I have **b**.

Who has the
first letter in
carrot?

I have **c**.

Who has the
first letter in
lion?

I have **l**.

Who has the
first letter in
jam?

I have **j**.

Who has the
first letter in
ice?

Who has the
first letter in
tomato?

I have **i**.

Who has the
first letter in
worm?

I have **t**.

Who has the
first letter in
elephant?

I have **w**.

Who has the
first letter in
door?

I have **e**.

Who has the
first letter in
octopus?

I have **d**.

I have **o**.

Who has the
first card?

I have the first card.

Who has the **zoo** animal that begins with l?

 I have .

Who has the **zoo** animal that begins with c?

 I have .

Who has the **zoo** animal that begins with b?

 I have .

Who has the **zoo** animal that begins with z?

 I have .

Who has the **zoo** animal that begins with m?

 I have .

Who has the **zoo** animal that begins with a?

I have  .

Who has the **zoo** animal

that begins with **e**?

I have  .

Who has the **zoo** animal

that begins with **p**?

I have  .

Who has the **farm** animal

that begins with **g**?

I have  .

Who has the **farm** animal

that begins with **c**?

I have  .

Who has the **farm** animal

that begins with **h**?

I have  .

Who has the **farm** animal

that begins with **ch**?

I have  .

Who has the **farm** animal that begins with **sh**?

I have  .

Who has the **farm** animal that begins with **p**?

I have  .

Who has the **ocean** animal that begins with **o**?

I have  .

Who has the **ocean** animal that begins with **wh**?

I have  .

Who has the **ocean** animal that begins with **sh**?

I have  .

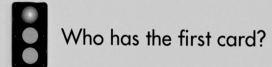 Who has the first card?

I have the first card.

Who has the picture that rhymes with frog?

I have

Who has the picture that rhymes with tree?

I have

Who has the picture that rhymes with star?

I have

Who has the picture that rhymes with cat?

I have

Who has the picture that rhymes with skate?

I have

Who has the picture that rhymes with sock?

I have

Who has the
picture that
rhymes with
snake?

I have

Who has the
picture that
rhymes with
truck?

I have

Who has the
picture that
rhymes with
fox?

I have

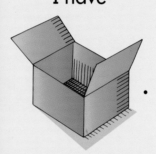

Who has the
picture that
rhymes with
fan?

I have

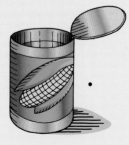

Who has the
picture that
rhymes with
moon?

I have

Who has the
picture that
rhymes with
book?

I have

Who has the picture that rhymes with pig?

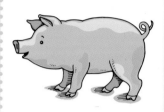

I have

Who has the picture that rhymes with stop?

I have

Who has the picture that rhymes with shell?

I have

Who has the picture that rhymes with rug?

I have

Who has the picture that rhymes with house?

I have

Who has the first card?

I have the first card.

Who has the odd one out?

I have  .

Who has the odd one out?

I have  .

Who has the odd one out?

I have  .

Who has the odd one out?

I have  .

Who has the odd one out?

I have  .

Who has the odd one out?

I have  .

Who has the odd one out?

I have  .

Who has the odd one out?

I have 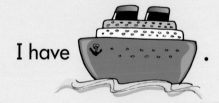 .

Who has the odd one out?

I have  .

Who has the odd one out?

I have  .

Who has the odd one out?

I have  .

 Who has the first card?

I have the first card.

Who has red?

I have **red**.

Who has black?

I have **black**.

Who has orange?

I have **orange**.

Who has brown?

I have **brown**.

Who has yellow?

I have **yellow**.

Who has white?

I have **white**.

Who has green?

I have **green**.

Who has purple?

I have **purple**.

Who has blue?

I have **blue**.

Who has gray?

I have **gray**.

Who has a rainbow?

I have **rainbow**.

Who has the first card?

I have the first card.

Who has the cat **on** a mat?

I have the cat **on** a mat.

Who has the cat **by** a hat?

I have the cat **by** a hat.

Who has the cat **in** a hat?

I have the cat **in** a hat.

Who has the cat **under** a table?

I have the cat **under** a table.

Who has the cat **between** the books?

I have the cat **between** the books.

Who has the cat **above** the books?

I have the cat **above** the books.

Who has the cat **behind** a tree?

I have the cat **behind** a tree.

Who has the cat **up** in a tree?

I have the cat **up** in a tree.

Who has the cat **in front of** a tree?

I have the cat **in front of** a tree.

Who has the cat **outside** a gate?

I have the cat **outside** a gate.

Who has the cat **inside** a cave?

I have the cat **inside** a cave.

Who has the first card?

I have the first card.

Who has the odd one out?

mom
mom
can
mom

I have **can**.

Who has the odd one out?

can
like
can
can

I have **like**.

Who has the odd one out?

is
is
is
see

I have **see**.

Who has the odd one out?

my
my
is
my

I have **is**.

Who has the odd one out?

the
my
the
the

I have **my**.

Who has the odd one out?

the
see
see
see

I have **the**.	Who has the odd one out? **to** **she** **she** **she**	I have **to**.	Who has the odd one out? **to** **on** **to** **to**
I have **on**.	Who has the odd one out? **and** **it** **and** **and**	I have **it**.	Who has the odd one out? **for** **for** **for** **she**
I have **she**.	Who has the odd one out? **and** **it** **it** **it**	I have **and**.	Who has the odd one out? **in** **in** **you** **in**

I have **you**. | Who has the odd one out?

his
go
go
go

I have **his**. | Who has the odd one out?

he
for
he
he

I have **for**. | Who has the odd one out?

at
at
at
in

I have **in**. | Who has the odd one out?

on
on
am
on

I have **am**. | Who has the odd one out?

be
at
be
be

I have **at**.

Who has the first card?

I have the first card.

Who has **c-a-t**?

I have  .

Who has **r-a-t**?

I have  .

Who has **b-a-t**?

I have  .

Who has **h-a-t**?

I have  .

Who has **m-a-t**?

I have  .

Who has **v-a-n**?

I have  .

Who has **c-a-n**?

I have .

Who has **f-a-n**?

I have .

Who has **p-a-n**?

I have .

Who has **p-i-n**?

I have .

Who has **f-i-n**?

I have .

Who has **r-u-n**?

I have  .

Who has **s-u-n**?

I have ☀ .

Who has **b-a-g**?

I have 🛍 .

Who has **t-a-g**?

I have  .

Who has **r-u-g**?

I have 🧿 .

Who has **b-u-g**?

I have  .

 Who has the first card?

I have the first card.

Who has the letters in the word **and**?

I have **a-n-d**.

Who has the letters in the word **at**?

I have **a-t**.

Who has the letters in the word **see**?

I have **s-e-e**.

Who has the letters in the word **like**?

I have **l-i-k-e**.

Who has the letters in the word **my**?

I have **m-y**.

Who has the letters in the word **to**?

I have **t-o**.

Who has the letters in the word **am**?

I have **a-m**.

Who has the letters in the word **is**?

I have **i-s**.

Who has the letters in the word **you**?

I have **y-o-u**.

Who has the letters in the word **can**?

I have **c-a-n**.

Who has the letters in the word **the**?

I have **t-h-e**.

 Who has the first card?

I Have, Who Has?: Language Arts • Gr. K © 2010 Creative Teaching Press